Sky Atlas

for
Small Telescopes and Binoculars

By
David S. Chandler
&
Billie E. Chandler

Published by David Chandler Company

The authors wish to thank John Gossett and Anthony Cook for their valuable suggestions and assistance with deep sky object selection, and Monsignor Ronald Royer for his advice on variable stars.

The Milky Way outlines were digitized from line drawings made by the renowned space artist Don Davis specifically for this project. Although the Milky Way is difficult to render as line drawings at all, Don's care and expertise have resulted in a substantial contribution to the overall impact and usefulness of this atlas.

All star maps for this atlas were produced using *Deep Space: The Observer's Guide to the Night Sky,* star mapping software.

Published by
David Chandler Co.
P.O. Box 999
Springville, CA 93265 USA
http://www.davidchandler.com

ISBN 978-1-891938-19-1

"Slowly, gently, night unfurls its splendor..."

PHANTOM OF THE OPERA
LYRICS BY CHARLES HART

The Splendor of the Night

The night sky is our window to the universe. The bright blue dome of the daytime sky blocks out the heavens and focuses our attention on the down-to-earth affairs of daily life. But the dark night sky, far from city lights, draws our vision outward.

With your eyes alone, on a dark moonless night, you can see about three thousand individual stars, the broad glowing band of the Milky Way, a few of the largest and brightest star clusters, and one galaxy besides our own (or three, if you are in the southern hemisphere).

The constellation patterns are fascinating to learn and they are important for what is to follow. They will be your stepping stones to the fainter "deep sky objects." The easiest way to familiarize yourself with the constellations is to use a star dial that can be set to match the sky for any hour of any night of the year. (We recommend *The Night Sky,* a star dial designed to show the sky with minimal distortion. See the resource list at the end of the atlas.)

If you own a small telescope or a pair of binoculars you have a wonderful resource for exploration and discovery. The best first "telescope" is actually a pair of binoculars. Binoculars, with their wide fields of view, allow you to easily explore the Milky Way, our home galaxy, with its intricate structure of bright star clouds interlaced with networks of dark dust lanes. Scattered along the Milky Way your binoculars will show you dozens of star clusters and glowing interstellar clouds called nebulae. Looking away from the Milky Way a number of additional galaxies can be brought into view.

A small telescope narrows the field of view, usually to 1° or less, but the tradeoff is higher power. The broad vistas are eliminated, but smaller individual objects can be brought into view. If you have a small telescope and binoculars, use them both. They complement each other nicely.

Why You Need This Star Atlas

After looking at the moon and possibly a planet or two, most small telescopes are packed away in closets, rarely to be used again, and most binoculars are never aimed upward in the first place. Without appropriate charts and reference materials deep sky objects can be very difficult to find. Randomly sweeping the sky with a small telescope will usually be a disappointing experience. The problem is that whereas the most common size "starter" telescopes sold are 2.5 inches in diameter, most star atlases are designed for use with telescopes at least 6 inches in diameter! It is true that a larger instrument is preferable, but unless beginners can experience some success with their first telescope they are unlikely to ever graduate to a larger one.

The goal of this atlas is to provide a selection of objects that can be seen and appreciated in even the smallest instruments: typical off-the-shelf binoculars and 2.5 inch telescopes. We have observed these objects ourselves over the years with many different instruments and provide first-hand commentary from field notes.

Setting the Stage

By "deep sky objects" we mean celestial objects beyond our solar system. You will undoubtedly want to observe the moon and planets first, because they are bright and easy to find, but you will soon want more. Deep sky objects include open star clusters, globular star clusters, bright and dark nebulae, planetary nebulae, supernova remnants, and galaxies. We have also included a number of interesting binary stars and a few other notable stars.

Deep sky objects tend to be faint, so your #1 goal should be to find a dark observing site. Judge your site by comparing the faintest stars visible in the sky with the magnitudes of the stars shown in the atlas. The ancient Greeks divided the naked eye stars into six brightness categories ranging from 1st magnitude, for the brightest stars, to 6th magnitude for the faintest stars visible under good conditions. Unless you can see down to at least 4th magnitude you will probably have difficulty seeing any but the brightest deep sky objects. A bright sky also limits the number of reference stars and will limit your ability to find faint objects. With the spread of light pollution from growing cities don't be surprised if you need to drive a considerable distance to find a suitable site.

A full moon is as bad as street lights when it comes to deep sky observing! Check your calendar and plan to observe when the moon is a thin crescent or out of the sky entirely. If the moon is bright, use the time to observe the moon and planets and save the fainter deep sky objects for another night. A first quarter moon will be overhead at sunset and set by midnight. A full moon is very bright and will be up all night. A third quarter moon will rise about midnight, leaving the first half of the night dark. New moon means *no moon* and is the ideal time for deep sky observing.

When you observe it is important to plan for your own physical comfort. Unless you are warm and relaxed your attention span will be severely limited. Dress warmly, especially covering your head, and have some snacks and something warm to drink available.

It is a good habit to keep records of your observations. Include in your notes a description of the sky conditions (darkness, transparency, and steadiness of the air), and what instrument and magnification you are using. Practice describing what you see in words, trying to compare objects and make distinctions. Try making simple pencil sketches of what you see. Don't worry if you are not a great artist. Your drawings and notes are for your own use. Taking notes and sketching at the eyepiece force you to pay closer attention to details, and in the end you will find you see much more.

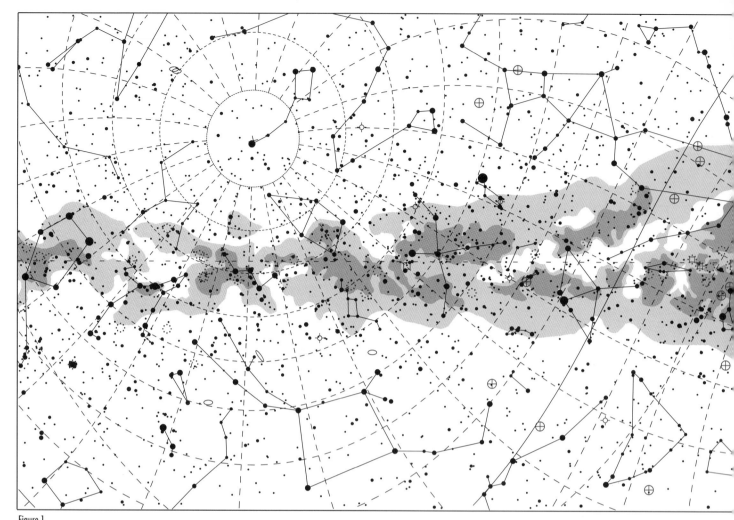

Figure 1.

Your Equipment

Get to know your instruments. A good exercise with binoculars is to trace out the constellations. You will find when looking at the Big Dipper in binoculars, for instance, that you will only see one star at a time. Learning to point your binoculars at the right spot in the sky takes some practice. The magnification and the extra stars that will be visible can cause you some confusion at first. Taking the time to trace out the constellations will give you more confidence and save you time in the long run.

Regardless of the advertised magnification of your telescope you will be using it most of the time with the lowest power eyepiece available. This will give you the largest possible field of view for finding objects, and it will provide adequate magnification to see most objects in the atlas. If you want to use high power on a small object, find it with low power first, then switch eyepieces.

The mechanical stability of your telescope mounting is as important as its optical quality. If it is a wobbly mounting you will have difficulty finding what you are looking for, or will easily lose it once it is found. Take the stability of the mounting into consideration before purchasing a telescope, and do whatever you can to improve its functioning before taking it out at night.

Make sure that the finder scope, in particular, is mounted securely and learn how to adjust it to align with the main telescope. This takes practice, so do it ahead of time. Sight on a distant object in daylight. You can maneuver a three-screw adjustment more easily if you loosen one screw while you simultaneously take up the slack with a second screw. Go back and forth using different pairs of screws and become familiar with the resulting movement of the crosshairs.

If you can spend a little extra money to improve your telescope, one of the best investments is a "zero power finder," such as a Telrad™ sight. This kind of device images an illuminated target right on the sky. It allows you to see exactly where your telescope is pointing without the added confusion of a magnified (and inverted) view in the finder scope.

Learn to focus your telescope by practicing in daylight. Be aware that some telescopes have a draw tube that extends out by hand before you can achieve focus with the focusing knob. Learn to relax your eye and let the telescope accommodate to your eye, rather than vice versa.

Daylight practice will also make you aware of how to move the telescope to slew the field of view. If your telescope has an even number of reflections (0 for a straight-through refractor, or 2 for a Newtonian reflector), the field of view will be rotated 180.° If it has an odd number of reflections (1 for a refractor with a star diagonal, or 3 for certain folded optics designs) the field of view will be a mirror image of the sky. Learning to move

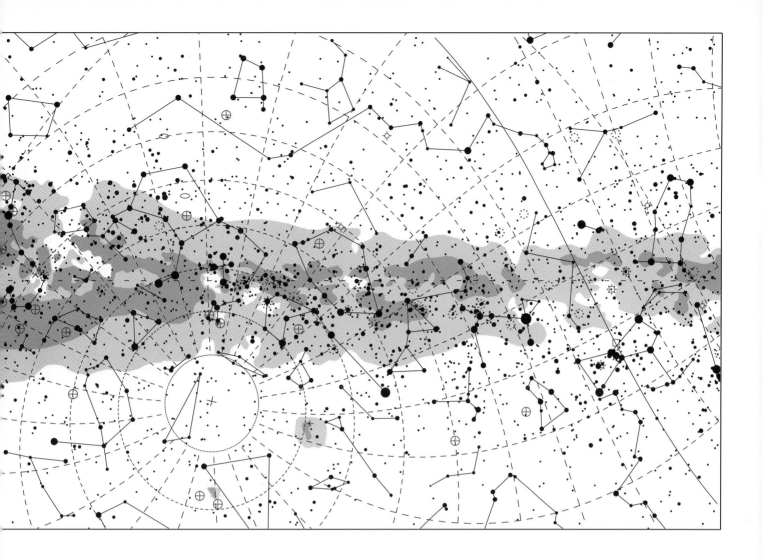

the telescope appropriately is trickier with a mirror image field of view. The key, again, is practice. If your telescope produces a mirror image field you will also have to take this into account when interpreting the small inset field-of-view maps in the atlas. One trick is to photocopy the charts, hold them face down, and read them by shining a flashlight upward through the paper.

The Milky Way

The most spectacular sight in the heavens is the Milky Way. Its mottled glow forms a complete band around the sky. Viewing the summer Milky Way high overhead on a pitch black moonless night is one of the greatest inspirational experiences offered by nature. Unfortunately city lights brighten the sky and mask it from view to the extent that the majority of the urban population has never witnessed this sight. If you are among that number you owe it to yourself to include a dark sky as a priority in your vacation plans.

The brightest stretch of Milky Way is seen at its best high overhead during the evening hours of mid summer. The fainter half of the band is best seen in mid winter. Figure 1 is a 360° wrap-around view of the sky oriented along the Milky Way rather than the celestial equator. Seen as a whole the Milky Way looks like an edge-on view of a galaxy, which is exactly what it is. It is our own galaxy seen from within. Our sun, with its

collection of planets, is one of the trillion or so stars in this giant system located about half way from the center toward one edge. The solar system is highly inclined to the plane of the galaxy. (Figure 2)

The blank areas along the Milky Way are not holes or gaps. They are caused by giant interstellar dust clouds in the foreground that block the view of what lies beyond. One such cloud forms an apparent rift from Cygnus through Serpens. Another blocks the view of the center of the galaxy, which would otherwise appear very bright, with stars highly concentrated toward a central point. Another very dark cloud, called the Coal Sack, lies near the Southern Cross. Another which lies between Sagittarius and Scorpius is called the "Pipe Nebula" which is also sometimes seen as the hind leg of the "Galactic Dark Horse." We have not catalogued the many dark nebulae among the deep sky objects in this atlas, but you will find many of them as you sweep the Milky Way with binoculars.

The Milky Way is the key to understanding the nature of the other deep sky objects. Notice how the various types of objects are distributed relative to the Milky Way. The numerous open clusters, represented by dotted circles, are distributed along the central band. Not many bright nebulae are shown because most of them are difficult to see in small instruments, but they have the same overall distribution as the open clusters.

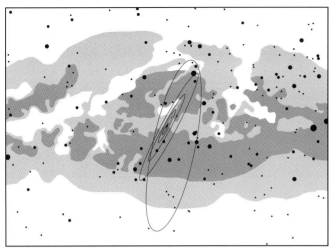

Figure 2.

(Bright nebulae are represented by small boxes. Frequently open clusters and nebulae are intermixed. These objects are represented by a combined nebula and open cluster symbol.)

The globular clusters, represented by circles with crosses through them, are distributed differently. They are not confined to the band of the Milky Way, but their distribution is centered around the center point of the galaxy which lies in the direction of Sagittarius. In three dimensions the Milky Way is basically a disk with a heavy concentration toward the center. The globular clusters occupy a spherical region surrounding the disk called the "galactic halo."

According to current thinking, the galaxy formed as a rotating spherical cloud. The globular clusters were part of the first burst of star formation activity. They formed together, hundreds of thousands at a time. As the galaxy rotated its clouds of dust and gas flattened, but the stars already formed retained their spherical distribution. Current star formation activity is confined to the disk of the galaxy where interstellar clouds of gas and dust are available as raw materials. As the clouds collapse they turn into clusters of stars. The newest clusters are actually seen embedded in gas clouds which are caused to glow by the hottest of the young stars of the cluster. Star formation today progresses at a slower rate, forming clusters of hundreds rather than hundreds of thousands of stars.

To summarize the geography of the Milky Way, we see it as a band because it is a disk being viewed edge-on. We see it wrap around the entire sky because we are seeing it from within. The Milky Way is brighter toward Sagittarius, where the distribution of globular clusters is also centered, because the galactic center lies in that direction and our solar system lies well out from the center along the disk. Our galaxy is about 100,000 light years across and we lie about 25,000 light years from the center.

Beyond the Milky Way

As seen in the sky, galaxies seem to avoid the Milky Way altogether. These huge islands of matter lie in the distant background, where distances are measured in millions of light years, rather than mere hundreds or thousands. The dust clouds of the Milky Way block the view of any galaxies behind them, but we

have two windows into the larger universe, north and south of the Milky Way band, where our view is relatively unobstructed.

Galaxies are not uniformly distributed through space. Rather, they clump together in clusters and groups of clusters known as superclusters. The Milky Way is part of a small galaxy cluster called the Local Group, consisting of about 25 galaxies. The Milky Way and the Andromeda Galaxy (M 31) are the two dominant members. The Local Group also contains the smaller Triangulum Galaxy (M 33), the two close companions of the Andromeda galaxies (M 32 and M 110), the Milky Way's companion galaxies (the Large and Small Magellanic Clouds) and an assortment of dwarf galaxies.

The nearest major galaxy cluster lies in the constellation Virgo with over a thousand members. Unfortunately most of the galaxies in this group are difficult in binoculars or a 2.5 inch telescope. We have included the three brightest members because of the significance of the group, but they should probably be classified as "challenge objects" in the context of this atlas.

The Virgo supercluster contains thousands of galaxies grouped in various sized clusters and including all of the bright galaxies in the sky. The main concentration of its galaxies forms a band around the sky almost perpendicular to the Milky Way, passing through Ursa Major, Virgo, Centaurus, crosses the Milky Way to pass through Eridanus, Sculptor, Cetus, and Andromeda. Our own local group is on the outer edges of the supercluster, so there are many more bright galaxies in one direction (looking out the northern window of the Milky Way toward Virgo) than in the opposite direction. Relatively few galaxies are listed in the atlas, because most require larger instruments to see, or at least to see well. Still you can recognize, even from the limited number accessible to small telescopes, a hint of the larger pattern to which they belong.

How to Use This Atlas

■   The atlas divides the sky into eight maps. Imagine slicing the top and bottom ends off an orange then sectioning the main body of the orange into six vertical slices. The north polar slice is Map 1. Maps 2 through 7 are north-south slices around the equator. Map 8 centers on the south celestial pole. For observers in most mid northern latitudes the sky shown on Map 1 is up all the time and the sky shown on Map 8 is never up. The following table is a rough guide to which atlas maps will be needed at various times of the year for observing during evening hours. Observing two

8:30 pm Mid Month	Map Number for...		
	Western Sky	Central Sky	Eastern Sky
January	2	3	4
March	3	4	5
May	4	5	6
July	5	6	7
September	6	7	2
November	7	2	3

hours later is like observing one month later.

■ Ideally this or any star atlas should be used in conjunction with a "star dial" (such as *The Night Sky*) which can be set not only by date, but also for any time of night. A star dial is most useful for identifying the constellations, figuring what will be up when, and planning future observing sessions. An atlas is most useful for finding specific objects within the constellations.

■ Most amateurs, especially when using binoculars or small telescopes, do not use setting circles with celestial coordinates to point their instruments. However some understanding of coordinates is useful simply for finding one's way around the atlas and coordinating between a star dial and the atlas. If you compare celestial coordinates to latitude and longitude on earth the simplest translation is between **latitude** on earth and **declination** in the sky. Both measure the angle above or below the equator, 0° being at the equator, 90° being at the north pole, and -90° being at the south pole. **Longitude** on earth measures in degrees east or west of the Royal Observatory in Greenwich England. In the sky the corresponding angle is called **right ascension**. It is measured eastward only and it is measured in hours rather than degrees. This just amounts to dividing the equator up into 24 pieces rather than 360 pieces.

■ One important item to note about the atlas maps is the southernmost declination you can see from your latitude (or northernmost declination if you are observing from the southern hemisphere). An observer at the north pole would see only northern hemisphere stars. In other words he would see stars down to the celestial equator. If he moved 10° south, where the latitude is 80°, he could see 10° below the celestial equator to declination -10°. An observer at 40° north latitude is 50° south of the north pole, so he could see to declination -50°. The rule is to subtract your latitude from 90° and change the sign. For those in the southern hemisphere the rule is to change the sign first, then subtract from 90°.

■ Each atlas map highlights certain objects in blue. These items are described on the opposite page. Most objects can be found easily from the main atlas map. In some cases, however, where the field is cluttered or an object is very small and may be overlooked at low power, a detailed finder chart is given as an inset map. The circles on the inset maps are either 1° low power telescope fields or 8° binocular fields as indicated. Actual field sizes will vary, but these values are typical.

■ When judging the expected brightness of an object you would of course look at the magnitude, but you have to take more into account. A large object (such as the face-on spiral galaxy M 33) may look bright in a table of data, but it will look very faint and diffuse in the sky. The problem is that since the object is so large, the available light is spread over a large area, thereby reducing the brightness per square degree, or "surface brightness." How visible a large object will be depends on how well it stands out against the brightness of the background sky. That is why a dark sky makes such a big difference.

■ On the back cover a number of celestial objects are shown in beautiful full color. When you look in your telescope, however, you will not usually see color. The colors are real, but you don't see them in color because the color sensors in your eyes

(the cone cells) are adapted to work best in bright daylight. A certain minimum amount of light is needed before they turn on. The cells for black and white vision (the rod cells), on the other hand can operate under very low light levels once they are dark adapted. That is why faint objects in your telescope or binoculars will generally look creamy white.

■ Related to the last point, since our eyes are primarily adapted for daytime conditions the center of vision on the retina (a spot called the fovea) is very dense with cone cells. This is where you focus your attention for fine detail work in bright light. At night looking at faint objects, however, this concentration of cone cells works against you. You will need to learn to use your peripheral vision to see faint objects.

■ The exception to the color issue is observing bright objects such as planets or double stars. Star colors indicate surface temperatures. Double stars frequently present highly contrasting colors side-by-side.

Where to Go from Here

If this atlas does the job it is intended to do, you will soon outgrow it. Your appetite will have been whetted and you may decide you want to go deeper. What are the next steps?

■ Subscribe to one or both of the major astronomy periodicals: *Sky and Telescope* and/or *Astronomy* and write for their catalogs.

■ Join a local astronomy club. *Sky and Telescope* magazine maintains a list of astronomy clubs and can refer you to one in your area.

■ Explore the astronomy resources on the World Wide Web. Start with our home page and follow the links. Our address is: http://www.DavidChandler.com

■ You will eventually want to buy a telescope with greater light grasp, but don't rush the process. If you learn to push your current equipment to its limit you will be a better observer and be more able to make good use of better equipment when you do buy it. Before you move into major equipment purchases join an astronomy club, go to one of the large national astronomy gatherings, get to know some other amateur astronomers and talk to them about their activities and equipment.

■ As you move to larger telescopes you will need more comprehensive reference materials. Some of the best printed star maps have been produced by Wil Tirion. His *Atlas 2000.0* is standard equipment among serious amateur astronomers, as is *Uranometria 2000.0.* A set of Wil Tirion's maps is included in the popular *Field Guide to the Stars and Planets* in the Peterson Field Guide series.

■ A growing alternative, or at least an important supplement, to printed star atlases is astronomical software. All the charts in this atlas were produced using *Deep Space: an Observer's Guide to the Night Sky,* which is available from us on CD ROM with an 18 million star database, thousands of galaxies, nebulae, and star clusters, orbital data for thousands of asteroids and comets, and the best star mapping features available. If you have a Mac, the program of choice is *Voyager.*

Name	Object Type	Mag	Size	# of Stars

CAMELOPARDALIS

NGC 1502	Open Cluster	5.7	8′	60

Fine cluster in a sparse area. Follow string of four stars to the cluster.

CANES VENATICI

M 106	Galaxy	8.3	18′×8′	(See Map 5)
M 51	Galaxy	8.4	11′×7.8′	(See Map 5)

CASSIOPEIA

Stock 2	Open Cluster	4.4	1°	50
+Mel 15	Open Cluster	6.6	21′	39
+NGC 1027	Open Cluster	6.7	20′	40

Group of three large to huge clusters near the Double Cluster. (See inset map.) They form an impressive group in binoculars. Too large for most telescopes.

NGC 663	Open Cluster	7.1	16′	100

Richest of several clusters along the "lazy" arm of the "W". Very nice in binoculars or a telescope with about 20 stars resolved against a fainter background glow.

NGC 457	Open Cluster	6.4	13′	200

A Canadian friend taught us to recognize this charming cluster as "The Little Critter" with two yellow eyes and outstretched arms.

NGC 7789	Open Cluster	6.7	16′	600

50 or 60 of the stars in this very rich cluster are bright enough to give it a grainy texture and the rest form a background glow. Binoculars show less texture.

M 52	Open Cluster	6.9	13′	170

Very rich thick patch with brighter stars standing out like sand grains against the background glow.

CEPHEUS

μ (Mu)	Red Star		

Herschel's "Garnet Star." Deep red-orange color.

δ (Delta)	Variable Star	3.6-4.3	

The prototype "Cepheid Variable" star, varying in a 5.3 day cycle. It is also a binary star with a blue Mag. 7.5 companion with 41″ separation.

Alfirk	Double Star	3.2, 7.8	14″ sep.

CYGNUS

NGC 6811	Open Cluster	6.8	13′	(See Map 7)
NGC 6826	Planetary Nebula	8.8	27″×24″	(See Map 7)
M 39	Open Cluster	4.6	32′	(See Map 7)

DRACO

ψ (Psi)	Double Star	4.6, 5.8	30.3″ sep.

Two yellow stars.

NGC 6543	Planetary Nebula	8.3	22″×16″

"Cat's Eye Nebula." Appears almost stellar at low power. See inset map for positive identification, then use moderately high power.

LACERTA

NGC 7243	Open Cluster	6.4	21′	(See Map 2)
NGC 7209	Open Cluster	6.7	25′	(See Map 2)

PERSEUS

NGC 1528	Open Cluster	6.4	18′	(See Map 3)
Mel 20	Open Cluster	1.2	3°	(See Map 3)
NGC 869	Open Cluster	4.3	30′	200
+NGC 884	Open Cluster	4.4	30′	150

(Also known as h & χ (Chi) Persei: "The Double Cluster") Both are large, rich clusters that can be seen naked eye and easily with binoculars or telescope.

URSA MAJOR

Mizar	Double Star	2.5, 4.0	14.4″ sep.

Naked eye or binoculars show Mizar and Alcor as an apparent double. Mizar is itself a real binary star visible with a small telescope. Both components are white.

M 101	Galaxy	7.7	26′

Large and bright, but diffuse face-on spiral galaxy. Best seen in binoculars. Too diffuse for small telescopes. Makes nearly an equilateral triangle with the last two stars of the handle of the Big Dipper.

M 81	Galaxy	6.9	26′×14′

One of the easiest spiral galaxies to see in a small telescope. Being partially tipped to our line of sight, it has an oval appearance.

M 82	Galaxy	8.4	11′×5′

An irregular galaxy just north of M81. Looks cigar-shaped. Both galaxies will usually fit in a single eyepiece field at low power.

URSA MINOR

Polaris	Notable Star		

A second magnitude star that happens to lie near the north celestial pole.

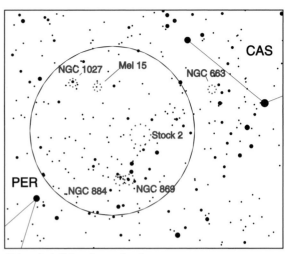

8° binocular field. Stars shown to Mag. 8.

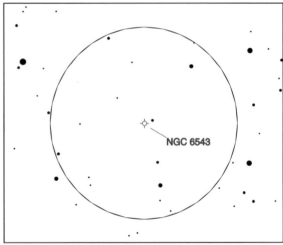

1° eyepiece field. Stars shown to Mag. 11.

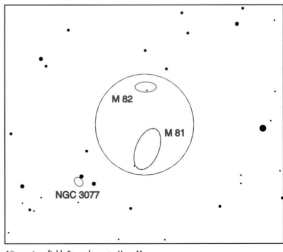

1° eyepiece field. Stars shown to Mag. 11.

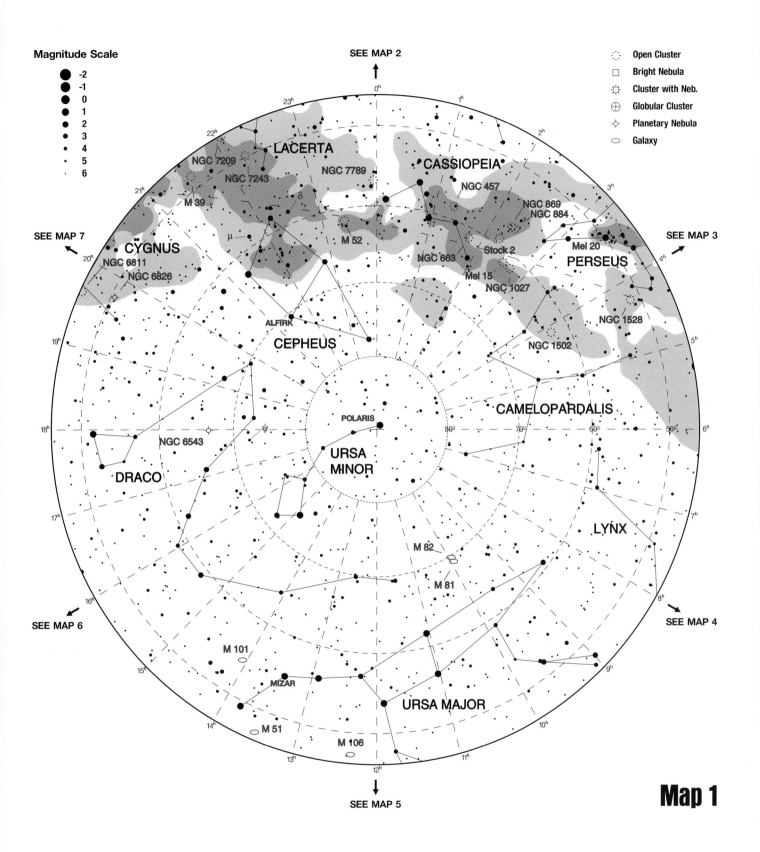

Map 1

Name	Object Type	Mag	Size	# of Stars

ANDROMEDA

Almach — Double Star — 2.3, 4.8 — 10″ sep.
(γ Andromedae) Beautiful gold and blue pair.

NGC 7662 — Planetary Nebula — 8.6 — 17″×14″
"Blue Snowball." Slightly fuzzy star at low power. See inset map for positive identification, then use moderately high power.

M 31 — Galaxy — 3.5 — 3°×1(
+M 32 — Galaxy — 8.2 — 8′×6′
+M 110 — Galaxy — 8.0 — 17′×10′
The Andromeda Galaxy and two small companions. M31 is the nearest large spiral galaxy. It is visible naked eye in a dark sky and easy in binoculars. M 32 is visible in binoculars as a small, concentrated cotton ball in a small telescope. M 110 is difficult in a small telescope. Even though it is brighter than M 32 it is larger and more diffuse. It is included here as a challenge.

NGC 752 — Open Cluster — 5.7 — 50′ — 75
Large, moderately rich cluster, best at low power or in binoculars. There are three prominent stars along the eastern side.

AQUARIUS

M 2 — Globular Cluster — 6.5 — 13′ — (See Map 7)
NGC 7293 — Planetary Nebula — 7.3 — 16′×12′
The "Helical" nebula. The largest planetary nebula. With its low surface brightness, it is easiest to see as an oval ring in binoculars.

ARIES

λ (Lambda) — Double Star — 4.8, 7.6 — 38″ sep.
White and blue pair.

CAPRICORNUS

M 30 — Globular Cluster — 7.5 — 11′ — (See Map 7)

CASSIOPEIA

Stock 2 — Open Cluster — 4.4 — 1° — (See Map 1)
NGC 457 — Open Cluster — 6.4 — 13′ — (See Map 1)
NGC 7789 — Open Cluster — 6.7 — 16′ — (See Map 1)

CETUS

Mira — Variable Star — 3-9 — (See Map 3)
NGC 246 — Planetary Nebula — 8.5 — 4′×4.5′
One of the larger planetary nebulae. In a telescope it forms an incomplete ring like the letter "C" with three stars enclosed.

CYGNUS

M 39 — Open Cluster — 4.6 — 32′ — (See Map 7)

LACERTA

NGC 7243 — Open Cluster — 6.4 — 21′ — 40
Loosely packed bright cluster against a rich Milky Way background.

NGC 7209 — Open Cluster — 6.7 — 25′ — 100
Parallel rows of bright stars make for a pretty cluster in the little lizard.

PEGASUS

NGC 7331 — Galaxy — 9.5 — 11.4′×4′
Elongated spiral galaxy with bright nucleus. The brightest in a large group of fainter galaxies.

M 15 — Globular Cluster — 6.3 — 12.3′ — (See Map 7)
Even though this nicely concentrated globular cluster is located on the edge of the chart, it is most easily found from the head of Pegasus, the "flying horse."

PERSEUS

NGC 869 — Open Cluster — 4.3 — 30′ — (See Map 1)
NGC 884 — Open Cluster — 4.4 — 30′ — (See Map 1)

PISCES

ψ (Psi) — Double Star — 5, 5 — 30″ sep.
ζ (Zeta) — Double Star — 4.2, 5.3 — 23.5″ sep.
Pale yellow and pink.

TX — Red Star — 6.9-7.7
Carbon star. Very red, variable brightness.

SCULPTOR

NGC 253 — Galaxy — 7.1 — 25′×7′
+NGC 288 — Globular Cluster — 8.1 — 14.8′
NGC 253 Looks like a smaller version of the Andromeda Galaxy. Best seen in binoculars, along with its globular cluster neighbor.

NGC 300 — Galaxy — 8.7 — 20′×15′
One of the largest galaxies in the sky. Although it is fairly bright overall, it has low surface brightness and is best seen in binoculars.

NGC 55 — Galaxy — 8.0 — 32′×6′
Very large, elongated barred spiral galaxy for your binoculars.

Name	Object Type	Mag	Size	# of Stars

TRIANGULUM

M 33 — Galaxy — 7.0 — 72′×45′
The "Pinwheel Galaxy," or "Triangulum Galaxy." Very large face-on spiral galaxy. Very difficult in a small telescope, but easy in binoculars in a dark sky.

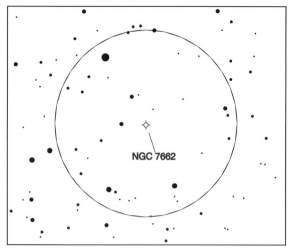

1° eyepiece field. Stars shown to Mag. 11.

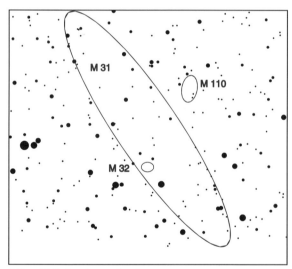

2.5° total field. Stars shown to Mag. 11.

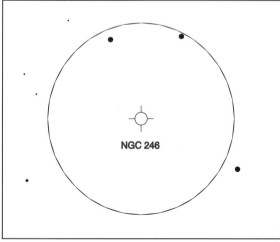

1° eyepiece field. Stars shown to Mag. 11.

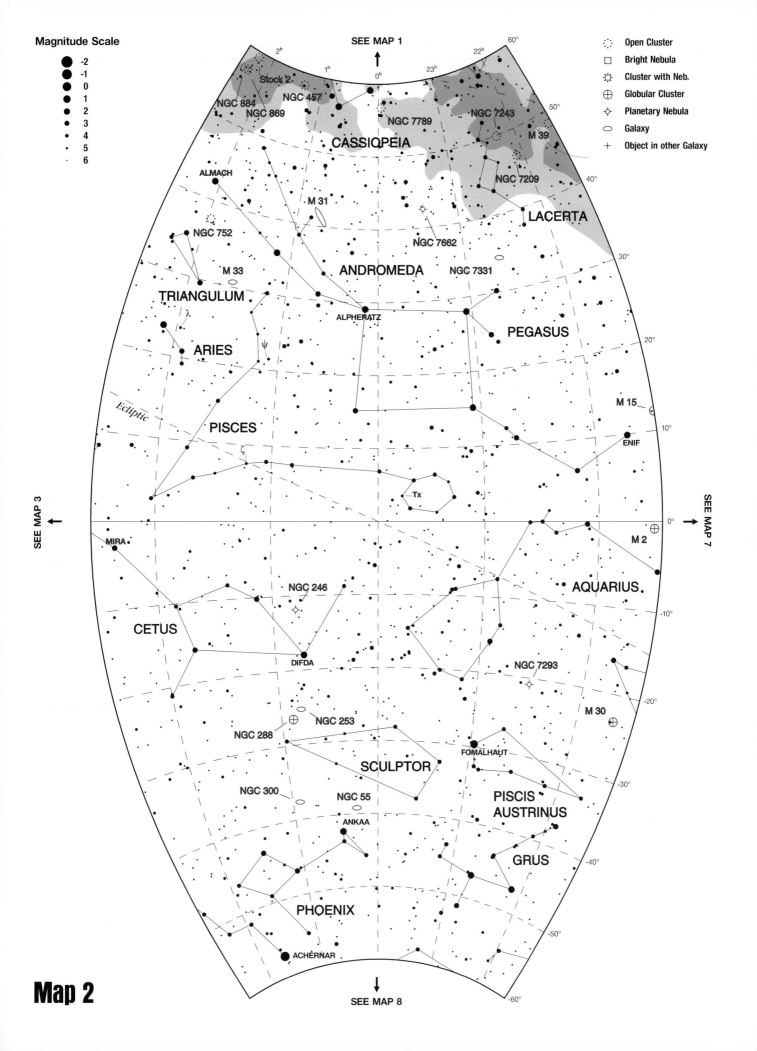

Map 2

Name	Object Type	Mag	Size	# of Stars

ANDROMEDA

Name	Object Type	Mag	Size	# of Stars
Almach	Double Star	2.3, 4.8	10" sep.	(See Map 2)
NGC 752	Open Cluster	5.7	50'	(See Map 2)

AURIGA

Name	Object Type	Mag	Size	# of Stars
M 38	Open Cluster	6.4	21'	160
+M 36	Open Cluster	6.0	12'	50
+M 37	Open Cluster	5.6	24'	590

This row of three magnificent clusters is accompanied by several smaller clusters visible in binoculars. Each has its own character. Examine each with a telescope and scan the field with binoculars.

CASSIOPEIA

Name	Object Type	Mag	Size	# of Stars
Stock 2	Open Cluster	4.4	1°	(See Map 1)

CETUS

Name	Object Type	Mag	Size	# of Stars
Mira	Variable Star	3-9	331 day average period	

A long period variable. The name means "Wonderful."

Name	Object Type	Mag	Size	# of Stars
M 77	Galaxy	8.8	7'×6'	

A small galaxy with high surface brightness and a very bright core. Galaxies with bright cores like this (called Seyfert galaxies) are thought to be related to quasars.

COLUMBA

Name	Object Type	Mag	Size	# of Stars
NGC 1851	Globular Cluster	7.3	11'	

(See note on M79 in Lepus.)

FORNAX

Name	Object Type	Mag	Size	# of Stars
NGC 1360	Planetary Nebula	7.0	6'×5'	

This is an unsual looking planetary: an oval haze resembling a galaxy more than anything else. It is similar in size to the Crab nebula (M 1 in Taurus) but brighter.

GEMINI

Name	Object Type	Mag	Size	# of Stars
M 35	Open Cluster	5.1	28'	(See Map 4)

LEPUS

Name	Object Type	Mag	Size	# of Stars
R	Variable/Red Star	5.5-11.7	431 day period	

Hind's "Crimson Star." A deep red carbon star. (See Inset Map).

Name	Object Type	Mag	Size	# of Stars
γ (Gamma)	Double Star	3.8, 6.4	1.5' sep.	

Yellow and garnet pair.

Name	Object Type	Mag	Size	# of Stars
M 79	Globular Cluster	8.0	8.7'	90,000

Most globular clusters are found in the Summer sky. M 79 and NGC 1851 nearby in Columba are the two best winter globulars. They are comparable in overall brightness and size, but differ in concentration. You may find M 79 easier to see in a small telescope. Neither can compare with the best globulars in the summer sky.

MONOCEROS

Name	Object Type	Mag	Size	# of Stars
NGC 2232	Open Cluster	3.9	45'	(See Map 4)

ORION

Name	Object Type	Mag	Size	# of Stars
M 42	Clstr w/Nebulosity	4.0	1.1°×1°	

M42 is the Great Orion Nebula. If you want one object that is easy to find, easy to see, and looks spectacular in even the smallest telescope, this is it. M 42 is the fuzzy middle "star" of the sword of Orion. The Trapezium is a multiple star system (with four main stars) in the heart of the nebula that illuminates it. Orion's sword also contains an open cluster at the north end and other patches of nebulosity. It is worth repeated scrutiny.

Name	Object Type	Mag	Size	# of Stars
Cr 70	Open Cluster	0.4	2.5°	100

The three belt stars of Orion are actually part of a huge star cluster that is far too big to be seen in a telescope. Binoculars will show scores of stars, including a giant "S" shaped chain connecting the two western-most stars of the belt.

Name	Object Type	Mag	Size	# of Stars
M 78	Bright Nebula	8.0	8'×6'	

This is a modest little nebula in contrast to M 42. It somewhat resembles a comet.

PERSEUS

Name	Object Type	Mag	Size	# of Stars
NGC 869	Open Cluster	4.3	30'	(See Map 1)
NGC 884	Open Cluster	4.4	30'	(See Map 1)
M 34	Open Cluster	5.2	35'	50

Large, rich cluster easily visible in binoculars or telescopes.

Name	Object Type	Mag	Size	# of Stars
Mel 20	Open Cluster	1.2	3°	50

Huge naked eye cluster in the heart of Perseus. Use binoculars.

Name	Object Type	Mag	Size	# of Stars
NGC 1342	Open Cluster	6.7	17'	100

The "3-finger" cluster. A moderately large grouping with three prominent chains.

Name	Object Type	Mag	Size	# of Stars
NGC 1528	Open Cluster	6.4	18'	160

Fairly large, irregular, rich cluster. Note circlet of stars at one end with "handle" at the other like an ice cream cone.

Name	Object Type	Mag	Size	# of Stars

TAURUS

Name	Object Type	Mag	Size	# of Stars
φ (Phi)	Double Star	5.1, 8.5	52" sep.	

Ruddy orange and lavender pair.

Name	Object Type	Mag	Size	# of Stars
Pleiades	Clstr w/Nebulosity	1.2	2°	250

M 45. The brightest and most conspicuous open cluster in the sky. (This is NOT the little dipper—a common mistake among beginners.) Binoculars show it well. It is larger than the field of most telescopes, but worth a look anyway. The nebulosity is a faint bluish haze.

Name	Object Type	Mag	Size	# of Stars
Hyades	Open Cluster	0.5	5.5°	380

The V-shaped head of the Bull (Taurus) is actually a huge naked eye open cluster...one of the nearest. Binoculars will show many additional stars.

Name	Object Type	Mag	Size	# of Stars
NGC 1647	Open Cluster	6.4	45'	120
+NGC 1746	Open Cluster	6.1	42'	20

These two clusters lie between the horns of the Bull. As you view the Hyades in binoculars, sweep to the northeast and these will be readily found. Note that the overall brightness of these two clusters is similar, but one shines with the combined light of many faint stars while the other consistes of fewer brighter stars.

Name	Object Type	Mag	Size	# of Stars
M 1	S.Nova Remnant	8.4	6'×4'	

This is the famous Crab nebula, the remnants of a supernova that was observed world-wide in 1054 A.D. It is difficult in sm3all telescopes because of its diffuse appearance. A dark sky makes a big difference.

TRIANGULUM

Name	Object Type	Mag	Size	# of Stars
M 33	Galaxy	7.0	72'×45'	(See Map 2)

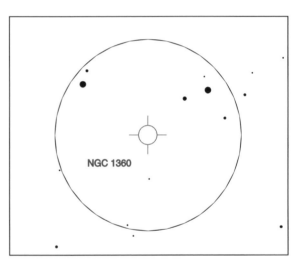

1° eyepiece field. Stars shown to Mag. 11.

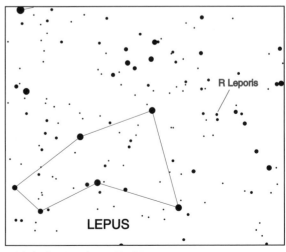

15° finder chart. Stars shown to Mag. 7.5.

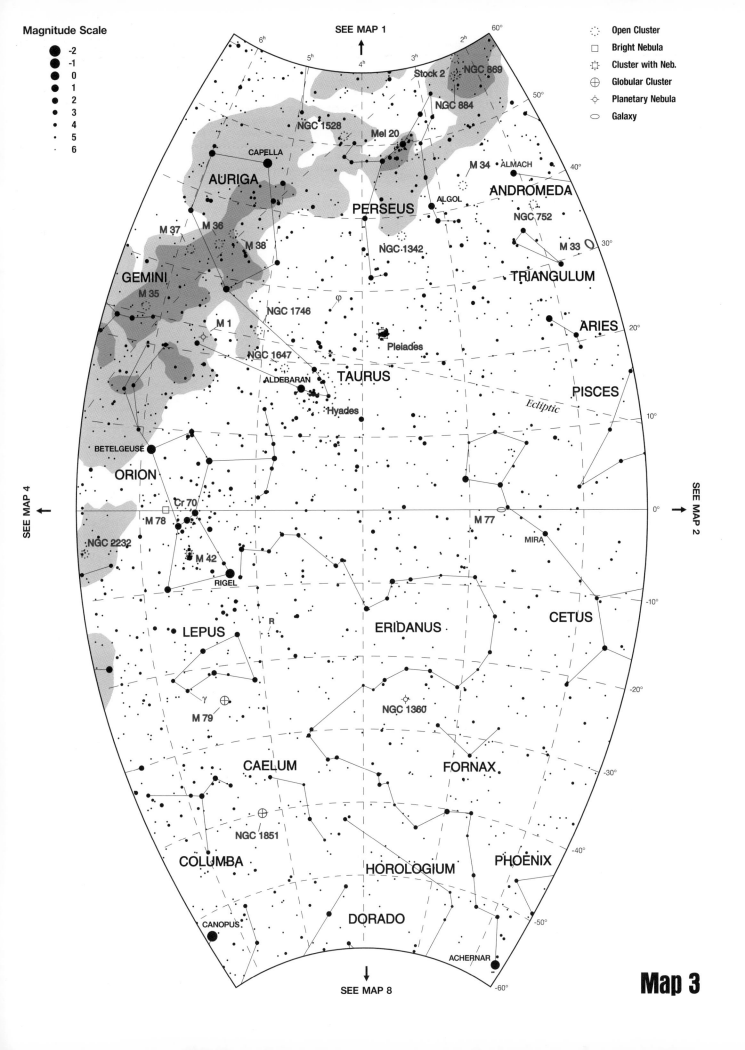

Map 3

Name	Object Type	Mag	Size	# of Stars

AURIGA

Name	Object Type	Mag	Size	# of Stars
M 36	Open Cluster	6.0	12′	(See Map 3)
M 37	Open Cluster	5.6	24′	(See Map 3)

CANCER

Name	Object Type	Mag	Size	# of Stars
τ (Iota)	Double Star	4.5, 6.5	30.5″ sep.	

Yellow and blue pair.

M 44	Open Cluster	3.1	1.6°	160

"Praesepe", the "Beehive." Too large for good telescope viewing, but excellent in binoculars. More conspicuous naked eye in a dark sky than the faint star pattern that makes up Cancer!

M 67	Open Cluster	6.9	30′	200

One of the oldest open clusters known. There appears to be a conspicuous hole just north of the center of the cluster.

CANIS MAJOR

Name	Object Type	Mag	Size	# of Stars
H3945	Double Star	5, 7	27″ sep.	

Beautiful orange and pale blue pair.

M 41	Open Cluster	4.5	32′	100

Beautiful bright, rich cluster about 4(south of Sirius. The Queen of the winter Milky Way.

NGC 2362	Open Cluster	4.1	8′	70

A beautiful symmetric speckled grouping surrounding the naked eye star Tau Canis Majoris. Don't miss this one!

Cr 140	Open Cluster	3.5	42′	30

Large but sparse grouping below the tail of the dog forming a distinctive "J" in binoculars.

GEMINI

Name	Object Type	Mag	Size	# of Stars
M 35	Open Cluster	5.1	28′	430

Rich open cluster easy in binoculars or telescope. A second tiny cluster 10 times farther away (NGC 2158) forms a superimposed smudge near one edge.

NGC 2392	Planetary Nebula	8.6	1.8′×1.7′	

The "Eskimo" nebula. A small planetary. Verify eyepiece field then use moderately high power. Milky bluish disk. (See inset map.)

HYDRA

Name	Object Type	Mag	Size	# of Stars
M 48	Open Cluster	5.8	54′	80

A large naked eye patch forming a well concentrated cluster with looser outer regions. Excellent in binoculars or telescope.

NGC 3242	Planetary Nebula	8.6	1.7′×1.6′	(See Map 5)

MONOCEROS

Name	Object Type	Mag	Size	# of Stars
β (Beta)	Triple Star	4.7, 5.2, 5.6 /	7″, 10″ sep.	
ε (Epsilon)	Double Star	4.5, 6.5	14″ sep.	

Gold and blue pair.

NGC 2232	Open Cluster	3.9	45′	40

A very bright but poorly concentrated gathering of about six bright stars and many fainter ones in an elongated north-south group.

NGC 2244	Clstr w/Nebulosity	4.8	24′	50

The "Rosette" nebula. A huge donut of diffuse nebulosity surrounds a ladder-shaped cluster. Use binoculars on a very dark night to see the nebulosity.

NGC 2264	Clstr w/Nebulosity	3.9	20′	140

The "Christmas Tree" cluster. A naked eye star forms the base of the tree. Visible in binoculars or telescope.

NGC 2301	Open Cluster	6.0	12′	75

Very striking, bright, easy cluster with about ten bright stars in a line with a concentration at the middle including a blue, gold and red trio of stars like jewels on a string.

M 50	Open Cluster	5.9	16′	150

Rich, concentrated open cluster above the northern ear of Canis Major, the "Large Dog." Good in binoculars or telescope.

ORION

Name	Object Type	Mag	Size	# of Stars
M 42	Clstr w/Nebulosity	4.0	1.1°×1°	(See Map 3)
Cr 70	Open Cluster	0.4	2.5°	(See Map 3)
M 78	Bright Nebula	8.0	8′×6′	(See Map 3)

PUPPIS

Name	Object Type	Mag	Size	# of Stars
M 46	Open Cluster	6.1	27′	220
+M 47	Open Cluster	4.4	30′	80

These two clusters are a beautiful contrasting pair: M 47, a loose gathering of bright stars, M 46, a much richer gathering of fainter stars. Both are nice clusters; the pair together is outstanding!

M 93	Open Cluster	6.2	13′	80

Lovely rich conglomeraton. Great in binoculars even though smaller than some other clusters in the region.

NGC 2451	Open Cluster	2.8	50′	150

PUPPIS (Cont.)

Name	Object Type	Mag	Size	# of Stars
+NGC 2477	Open Cluster	5.8	43′	1900!

An easy naked eye pair one telescope field apart. 2477 is beautiful in a telescope. It is reputed to be the richest open cluster, consisting of a uniform array of fainter stars. 2451 is a sparser but brighter grouping. Compare this pair with M 46-47.

NGC 2539	Open Cluster	6.5	22′	50

In a small telescope, about 30 stars are highlighted against a grainy glow. A beautiful yellow star lies on the NE edge.

NGC 2546	Open Cluster	6.3	1°	40

A large, loose, oval grouping, nice in binoculars. The stars come in bright, loose bunches.

TAURUS

Name	Object Type	Mag	Size	# of Stars
M 1	S.Nova Remnant	8.4	6′×4′	(See Map 3)

VELA

Name	Object Type	Mag	Size	# of Stars
NGC 2547	Open Cluster	4.7	20′	80
+IC 2391	Open Cluster	2.5	50′	30

The Milky Way from Puppis through Vela and Carina is peppered with bright open clusters such as these. Sweep with binoculars and follow up with a telescope.

NGC 3132	Planetary Nebula	8.2	1.4′×1.9′	

Another planetary with a bright center reminiscent of the "Eskimo" nebula in Gemini. (See inset map.)

NGC 3201	Globular Cluster	6.8	18.2′	

Appears as an unconcentrated glow of moderate size.

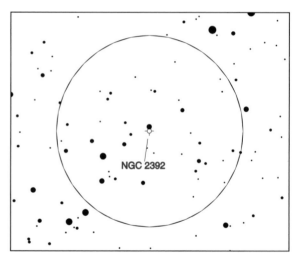

1° eyepiece field. Stars shown to Mag. 11.

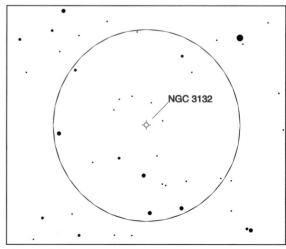

1° eyepiece field. Stars shown to Mag. 11.

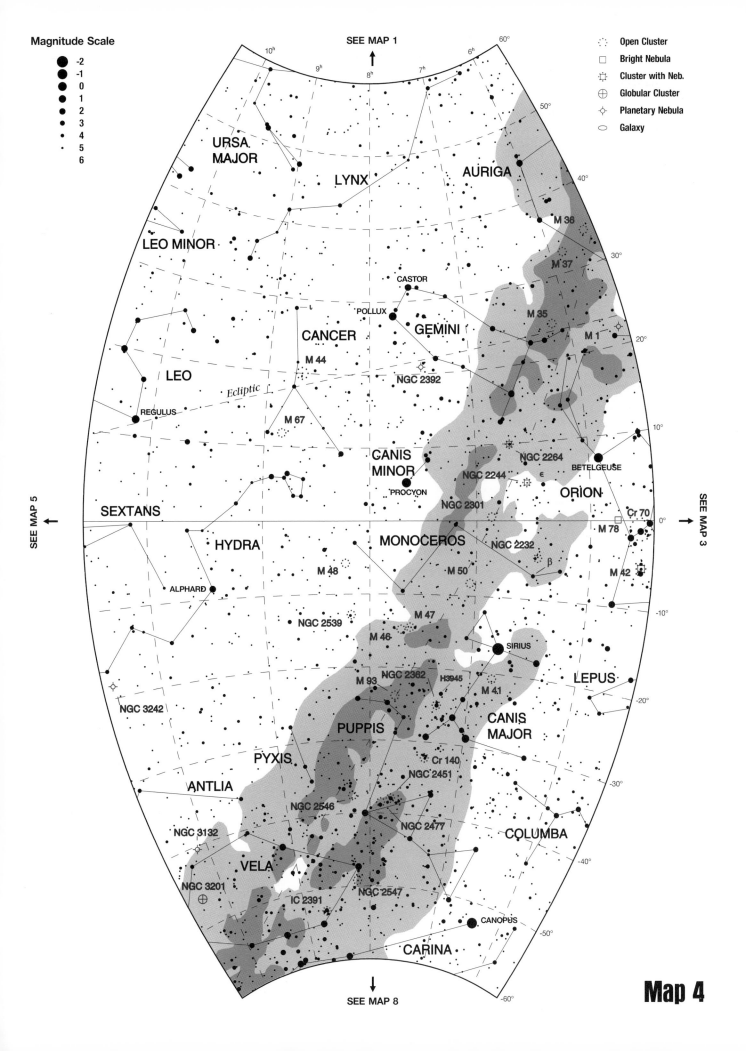

Map 4

Name	Object Type	Mag	Size	# of Stars

CANES VENATACI

Cor Caroli — Double Star — 3, 5.5 — 20″ sep.
Yellow and Lilac pair.

M 106 — Galaxy — 8.3 — 18′×8′
Near edge-on spiral with a brighter nucleus.

NGC 4490 — Galaxy — 9.7 — 6′×3′
An irregular large oval galaxy interacting with a small galaxy.

M 94 — Galaxy — 8.1 — 11′×9′
Broad oval, almost round face-on spiral.

M 63 — Galaxy — 8.6 — 12′×7.5′
Elongated oval; brighter in the middle.

M 51 — Galaxy — 8.4 — 11′×7.8′
Classic face-on spiral with two arms. Interacting with a smaller galaxy. Both are visible in binoculars against a dark sky.

M 3 — Globular Cluster — 5.9 — 16′ — 140,000
A first rate globular cluster with a bright core.

CARINA

NGC 3293 — Open Cluster — 4.7 — 6′ — (See Map 8)
NGC 3532 — Open Cluster — 3.0 — 55′ — (See Map 8)

CENTAURUS

NGC 5128 — Galaxy — 7.0 — 18′×14′
Large spherical galaxy with an unusual dark band across its equator. We call it the "Hamburger."

ω (Omega) — Globular Cluster — 3.7 — 36.3′ — 5,000,000
One of the two most spectacular globular clusters in the entire sky. The other is 47 Tucanae. They are about equal in size and brightness, but whereas Omega Centauri is evely bright, "47 Tuc" brightens dramatically toward the center.

NGC 5460 — Open Cluster — 5.6 — 25′ — 40
A striking grouping of bright stars stretched into a short chain.

COMA BERENICES

Mel 111 — Open Cluster — 1.8 — 4.6°— 80
This is the "Hair" of Berenice that gave the constellation its name. An easy, large Y-shaped naked eye cluster to be appreciated in binoculars as well. Frequently overlooked in sky atlases because it is too large for telescope viewing.

M 64 — Galaxy — 8.5 — 9′×5′
The "Black Eye" galaxy. Oval with brighter nucleus. In larger scopes a black patch is visible which gives it its name.

M 53 — Globular Cluster — 7.7 — 13.6′ — 200,000
Easy globular in binoculars or telescope.

CORVUS

Algorab — Double Star — 3, 8.5 — 24″ sep.
Yellow and pale lavender pair.

HYDRA

NGC 3242 — Planetary Nebula — 8.6 — 1.7′×1.6′
"Ghost of Jupiter." Pale blue, bright, small planetary. Use inset chart to verify field, then use moderately high power.

M 68 — Globular Cluster — 8.2 — 12′ — >100,000
Small but rich globular cluster with a highly concentrated core.

M 83 — Galaxy — 8.2 — 11′×10′
Diffuse disk, visible in binoculars. This is a large face-on barred spiral galaxy.

LEO

M 65 — Galaxy — 9.3 — 10′×3.3′
+M 66 — Galaxy — 9.0 — 8.7′×4.4′
Along with the fainter NGC 3628, this trio is known by some as the "Leo Droppings." Use inset map and look for the "man in a chair" asterism.

URSA MAJOR

Mizar — Double Star — 2.5, 4.0 — 14.4″ sep. — (See Map 1)
M 101 — Galaxy — 7.7 — 26′ — (See Map 1)

VELA

NGC 3132 — Planetary Nebula — 8.2 — 1.4′×1.9′ — (See Map 4)
NGC 3201 — Globular Cluster — 6.8 — 18.2′ — (See Map 4)

VIRGO

M 87 — Galaxy — 8.6 — 7.2′×6.8′
+M 86 — Galaxy — 9.2 — 7.4′×5.5′
+M 84 — Galaxy — 9.3 — 5′×4.4′
Three of the brightest galaxies of the rich Virgo cluster. Difficult in a 2.5″, but an excellent group to be aware of when you move up to a larger scope.

M 104 — Galaxy — 8.3 — 8.9′×4.1′
The "Sombrero" galaxy. Elongated galaxy with a fat but diffuse central bulge.

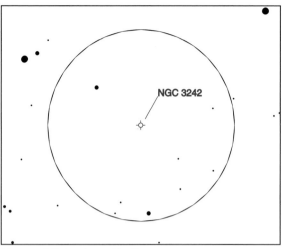

1° eyepiece field. Stars shown to Mag. 11.

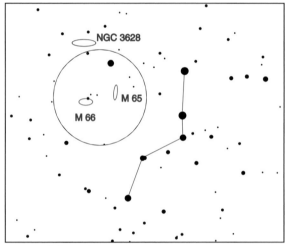

1° eyepiece field. Stars shown to Mag. 11.

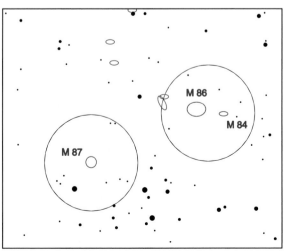

Two 1° eyepiece fields. Stars shown to Mag. 11.

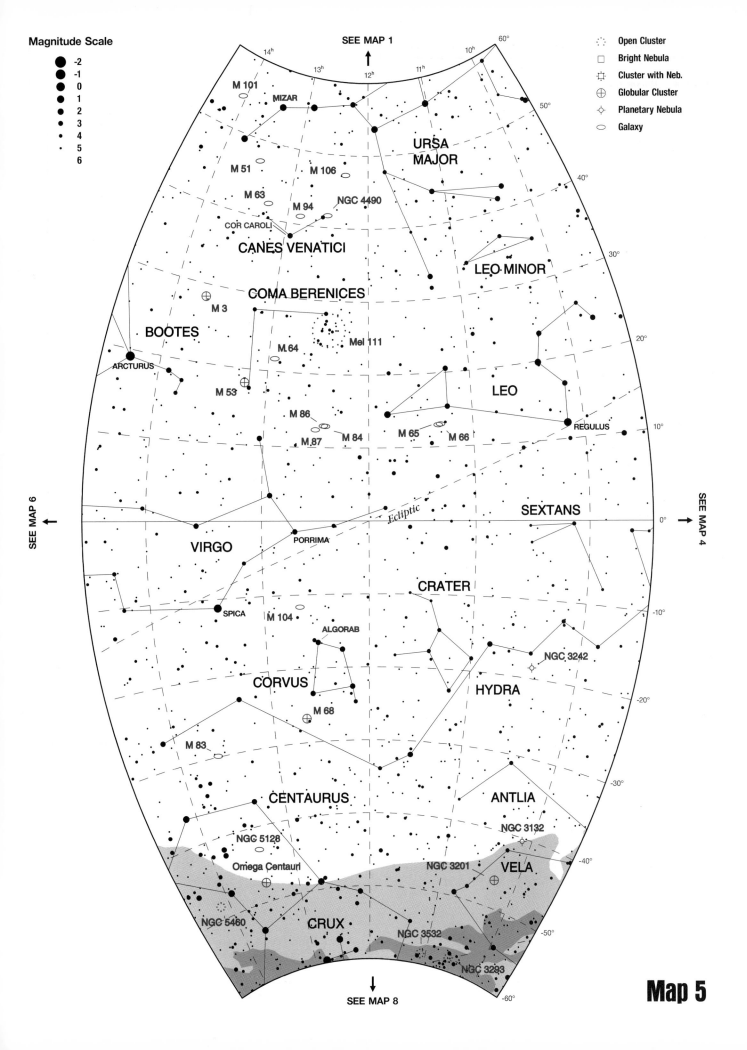

Map 5

Name	Object Type	Mag	Size	# of Stars

ARA
| NGC 6397 | Globular Cluster | 5.7 | 26.7′ | (See Map 8) |

CANES VENATICI
| M 3 | Globular Cluster | 5.9 | 16′ | (See Map 5) |

CENTAURUS
| NGC 5460 | Open Cluster | 5.6 | 25′ | (See Map 5) |

CORONA AUSTRALIS
| NGC 6541 | Globular Cluster | 6.6 | 13.1′ | (See Map 7) |

HERCULES
| M 13 | Globular Cluster | 5.9 | 17.6′ | 500,000 |

One of the best globulars. A favorite for northern observers.

| M 92 | Globular Cluster | 6.5 | 11.2′ | 250,000 |

One of the most overlooked globulars because of its proximity to M 13, its more famous neighbor. M 92 is more concentrated toward the center.

HYDRA
| M 83 | Galaxy | 8.2 | 11′×10′ | (See Map 5) |

NORMA
| NGC 6067 | Open Cluster | 5.6 | 13′ | (See Map 8) |

OPHIUCHUS
ο (Omicron)	Double Star	5.2, 6.8	10.2″ sep.	
M 12	Globular Cluster	6.6	15′	
+M 10	Globular Cluster	6.6	15′	

These neighboring twins are very similar in size, brightness, and concentration.

| M 62 | Globular Cluster | 6.6 | 14.1′ | |
| +M 19 | Globular Cluster | 7.2 | 6′×4.5′ | |

M 19 is very oval and both of these neighbors have somewhat off-center cores.

| M 9 | Globular Cluster | 7.9 | 9.3′ | 60,000 |

Concentrated with a slightly oval appearance.

| M 14 | Globular Cluster | 7.6 | 12.7′ | |

Large bright central region with diffuse halo.

| IC 4665 | Open Cluster | 4.2 | 41′ | 30 |

Large, sparse but bright open cluster. Use binoculars.

SAGITTARIUS
M 23	Open Cluster	5.5	27′	(See Map 7)
M 20	Clstr w/Nebulosity	6.3	28′	(See Map 7)
M 8	Clstr w/Nebulosity	4.6	1.3°×0.7°	(See Map 7)
M 21	Open Cluster	5.9	13′	(See Map 7)
M 24	Open Cluster	4.0	2°×1.5°	(See Map 7)
M 17	Clstr w/Nebulosity	6.0	45′×35′	(See Map 7)
M 28	Globular Cluster	6.9	11.2′	(See Map 7)

SCORPIUS
| υ (Nu) | Double Star | 4, 6.2 | 41.4″ sep. | |

The components themselves are each double but difficult in a small telescope.

| M 80 | Globular Cluster | 7.2 | 8.9′ | 190,000 |
| +M 4 | Globular Cluster | 5.9 | 26.3′ | |

These neighboring globulars show sharp contrasts. M 4 is large and diffuse, while M 80 is small and concentrated. Both are easy targets.

| NGC 6124 | Open Cluster | 5.8 | 29′ | 100 |

A rich cluster with a concentrated central area.

Cr 316	Open Cluster	3.4	1.8°	
+NGC 6231	Open Cluster	2.6	15′	
+NGC 6242	Open Cluster	6.4	9′	

This cluster of clusters we call the "False Comet," referring to its naked eye appearance. The whole field is rich for sweeping with binoculars or a telescope.

| NGC 6388 | Globular Cluster | 6.8 | 8.7′ | |

A small diffuse cotton ball easy to find under the tail of the Scorpion.

| NGC 6441 | Globular Cluster | 7.4 | 7.8′ | |

A small globular cluster notable primarily because of its location by the stinger of the Scorpion.

| M 7 | Open Cluster | 3.3 | 1.3° | 55 |
| +M 6 | Open Cluster | 4.2 | 33′ | 330 |

Two of the nicest naked eye clusters in the summer Milky Way. Both are excellent binocular objects.

SERPENS
| M 5 | Globular Cluster | 5.8 | 17.4′ | 250,000 |

Large, rich, beautiful globular.

| M 16 | Clstr w/Nebulosity | 6.0 | 25′ | (See Map 7) |

URSA MAJOR
| M 101 | Galaxy | 7.7 | 26′ | (See Map 1) |

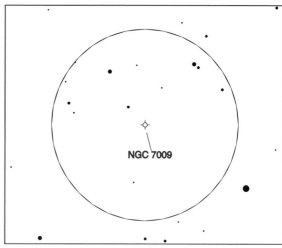

1° eyepiece field. Stars shown to Mag. 11.

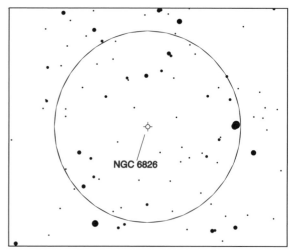

1° eyepiece field. Stars shown to Mag. 11.

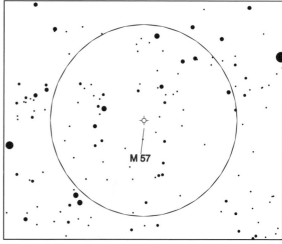

1° eyepiece field. Stars shown to Mag. 11.

THESE INSET MAPS REFER TO MAP 7.

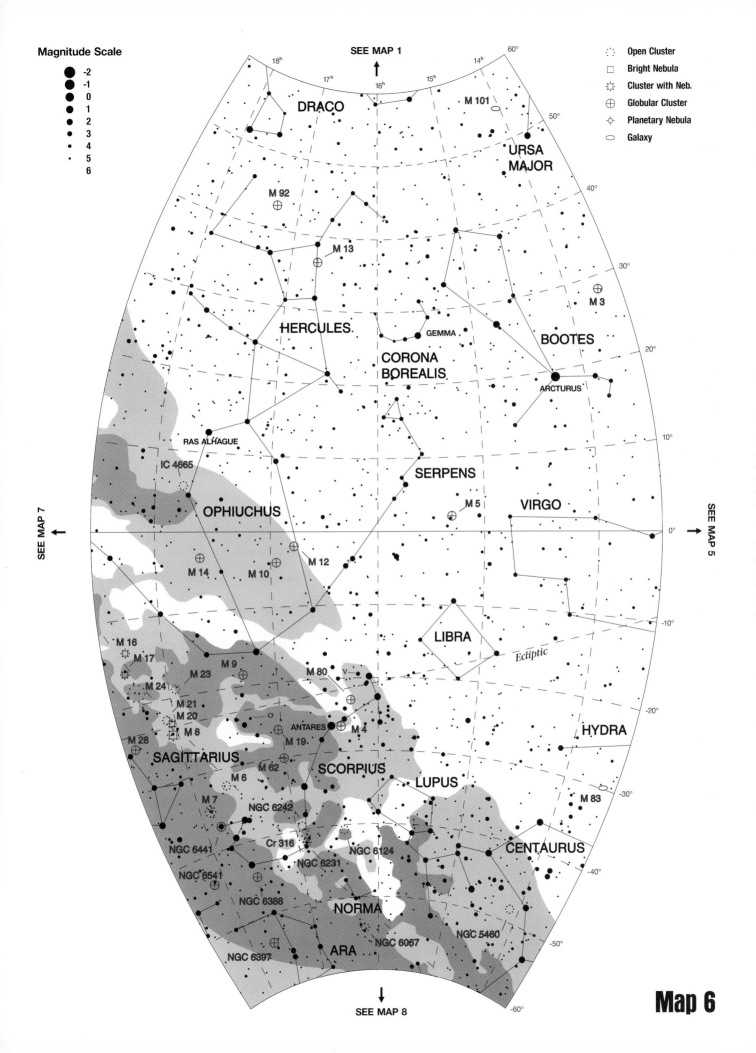

Map 6

Name	Object Type	Mag	Size	# of Stars

AQUARIUS

NGC 7009 — Planetary Nebula — 8.3 — 44"×23"
Called the "Saturn Nebula" because of its elongated appendages resembling Saturn's rings. Identify it within the field using the inset charts, then magnify.

M 2 — Globular Cluster — 6.5 — 13' — 500,000
A concentrated cotton ball without a sharp center.

AQUILA

NGC 6709 — Open Cluster — 6.7 — 13' — 110
Appears as a glowing patch in binoculars.

ARA

NGC 6397 — Globular Cluster — 5.7 — 26.7' — (See Map 8)

CAPRICORNUS

Dabih — Double — 3.1, 6 — 3.4' sep.
Orange-yellow and blue. Easy in binoculars.

M 30 — Globular Cluster — 7.5 — 11'
A small concentrated glow.

CORONA AUSTRALIS

NGC 6541 — Globular Cluster — 6.6 — 13.1'
A nicely concentrated globular.

CYGNUS

Albireo — Double Star — 3, 5.5 — 35" sep.
Beautiful contrasting color pair: blue and gold.

o¹ (Omicron)Trio — 4, 7, 5 — 1.8', 5.5' sep.
An optical group only, but worth noting. Lavender, green, and yellow.

61 — Double Star — 5.2, 6 — 30" sep.
A famous and notable double. The orbital period is about 700 years.

NGC 6811 — Open Cluster — 6.8 — 13' — 250
A nice binocular cluster off the western wing of Cygnus, the "Swan."

NGC 6826 — Planetary Nebula — 8.8 — 27"×24"
The "blinking planetary." A diffuse disk surrounds a bright central star. Looking directly at it reveals the star. Peripheral vision reveals the disk. Use the inset chart for positive identification, then use moderate power.

M 29 — Open Cluster — 6.6 — 7' — 81
In a telescope this loose cluster is almost impossible to pick out from the rich Milky Way background. Binoculars, however, show it as a cluster.

NGC 7000 — Bright Nebula — — — 2°×1.7°
The "North American Nebula." This is a huge and very diffuse nebula, included here for binoculars and black skies only. A dark foreground dust cloud carves out the Gulf of Mexico.

M 39 — Open Cluster — 4.6 — 32' — 30
A large, loose triangular arrangement of brighter stars against a rich Milky Way background. Try this in binoculars.

LACERTA

NGC 7209 — Open Cluster — 6.7 — 25' — (See Map 2)
NGC 7243 — Open Cluster — 6.4 — 21' — (See Map 2)

LYRA

ε (Epsilon) — Double-double — 5,6,5.2,5.5 — 3.5'/2.8",2.6"
The wide pair is easy even in binoculars. The close pairs are difficult.

M 57 — Planetary Nebula — 9.0 — 1.4'×1'
The "Ring" nebula. It lies 1/3 of the way between two bright stars in Lyra. In a small telescope it sppears as a tiny disk at low power. Magnify to see the ring.

OPHIUCHUS

M 14 — Globular Cluster — 7.6 — 12.7' — (See Map 6)
IC 4665 — Open Cluster — 4.2 — 41' — (See Map 6)

PEGASUS

M 15 — Globular Cluster — 6.3 — 12.3' — (See Map 2)
A beautifully concentrated cluster, brightening sharply toward the center.

SAGITTA

M 71 — Globular Cluster? — 8.3 — 7.2'
A compact grouping intermediate between an open and a globular cluster.

SAGITTARIUS

NOTE: When looking toward Sagittarius you are looking toward the center of the Milky Way galaxy. The Milky Way and its treasures are especially concentrated in this direction. See the Milky Way panorama map.

M 8 — Clstr w/Nebulosity — 4.6 — 1.3°×0.7° — 110
The "Lagoon" nebula. The brightest nebula in the summer sky visible from the northern hemisphere. It envelops a bright star cluster and is divided by a dark lane of dust. Look for an hourglass shaped region in the brightest part of the nebulosity.

SAGITTARIUS (Cont.)

M 20 — Clstr w/Nebulosity — 6.3 — 28' — 65
The "Trifid" nebula: a round patch of nebulosity with a Y-shaped dark lane pattern in it. Find it by moving slightly northward from M 8.

M 23 — Open Cluster — 5.5 — 27' — 130
A large, bright, and very rich grouping.

M 21 — Open Cluster — 5.9 — 13' — 70
This cluster lies in the same field of view as the Trifid nebula (M 20). It is a loose, oblong open cluster.

M 24 — Star Cloud — 4.0 — 2°×1.5°
This is actually a dense area of the Milky Way easily identified naked eye. In a telescope, look for black patches against the bright background caused by foreground dust clouds.

M 17 — Clstr w/Nebulosity — 6.0 — 45'×35' — 660
The "Swan" nebula, also called the "Omega" nebula. It appears as a bright patch with binoculars and a figure "2" shape with an extended base in a telescope, which resembles a floating swan.

M 22 — Globular Cluster — 5.1 — 24' — 500,000
The brightest globular cluster in this region. Easy in binoculars and better in a telescope.

M 28 — Globular Cluster — 6.9 — 11.2' — 50,000
An easy-to-find globular cluster just above the star forming the lid of the "Teapot."

M 25 — Open Cluster — 4.6 — 32' — 600
A large, bright cluster in a rich star field north from M 22.

M 69 — Globular Cluster — 7.7 — 7.1'
+M 70 — Globular Cluster — 8.1 — 7.8'
+M 54 — Globular Cluster — 7.7 — 9.1'
These three globulars constitute the "Teapot Scum." They are decent globular clusters in their own right even if they pale by comparison with the more spectacular objects in the Sagittarius region.

NGC 6723 — Globular Cluster — 7.3 — 11'
Technically included with Sagittarius, this globular is found closer to Corona Australis. It appears bright in the middle but weakly concentrated.

M 55 — Globular Cluster — 7.0 — 19' — 100,000
Very rich with bright middle and wispy edges. Find it with binoculars by following the outer two handle stars of the Teapot.

SCORPIUS

NGC 6388 — Globular Cluster — 6.8 — 8.7' — (See Map 6)
M 6 — Open Cluster — 4.2 — 33' — (See Map 6)
NGC 6441 — Globular Cluster — 7.4 — 7.8' — (See Map 6)
M 7 — Open Cluster — 3.3 — 1.3° — (See Map 6)

SCUTUM

M 11 — Open Cluster — 5.8 — 14' — 680
The "Wild Duck" cluster. This very rich open cluster has a single bright star standing out prominently in the middle surrounded by a dense pattern of fainter stars of uniform brightness. It is one of our favorite open clusters!

M 26 — Open Cluster — 8.0 — 15' — 120
A small but easy to find concentrated group.

SERPENS

M 16 — Clstr w/Nebulosity — 6.0 — 25' — 540
The "Eagle" nebula. A scattered cluster embedded in a nebula. In binoculars you can detect the glow of the nebula, but in a small telescope it is the cluster that stands out.

VULPECULA

Cr 399 — Open Cluster — 3.6 — 1° — 40
The "Coathanger" cluster. An east-west line of stars with a hook in the middle making a very nice coathanger! This one is for binoculars. It is too large for most telescope fields.

M 27 — Planetary Nebula — 7.3 — 8'×6.7'
The "Dumbell" nebula. We call it the "Apple Core." This is one of the brightest planetary nebulae.

NGC 6940 — Open Cluster — 6.3 — 31' — 170
A nice binocular object easily found from the eastern wing of the flying swan pattern of Cygnus.

(The inset maps for Map 7 are found with the notes for Map 6.)

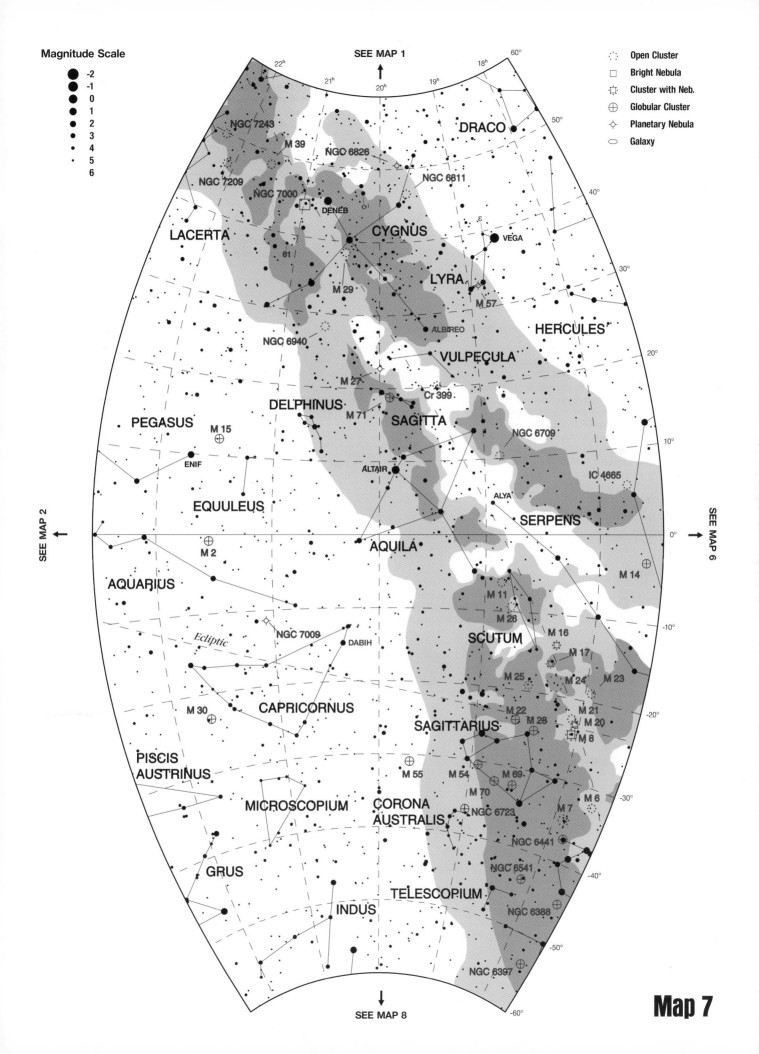

Magnitude Scale

-2
-1
0
1
2
3
4
5
6

Open Cluster
Bright Nebula
Cluster with Neb.
Globular Cluster
Planetary Nebula
Galaxy

DRACO

22ʰ
21ʰ
20ʰ
19ʰ
18ʰ
60°
50°

NGC 7243
M 39
NGC 6826
NGC 6811
40°

NGC 7209
NGC 7000
DENEB
VEGA

LACERTA
CYGNUS
LYRA
30°

61
M 29
M 57
HERCULES

ALBIREO
20°

NGC 6940
VULPECULA

M 27
Cr 399

DELPHINUS
M 71
SAGITTA
NGC 6709
10°

PEGASUS
M 15
IC 4665

ENIF
ALTAIR
ALYA
SERPENS

EQUULEUS
0°

AQUILA

M 2
M 14

AQUARIUS

M 11
M 26
-10°

Ecliptic
NGC 7009
DABIH
M 16
SCUTUM
M 17

M 25
M 24
M 23

M 22
M 21
-20°
M 30
CAPRICORNUS
M 28
M 20

SAGITTARIUS
M 8

PISCIS
AUSTRINUS
M 55
M 54
M 69
M 6
-30°

M 70
M 7

MICROSCOPIUM
CORONA
AUSTRALIS
NGC 6723

NGC 6441

GRUS
NGC 6541
-40°

TELESCOPIUM
NGC 6388

INDUS

-50°

NGC 6397

-60°

Map 7

Name	Object Type	Mag	Size	# of Stars

ARA

NGC 6397 — Globular Cluster — 5.7 — 26.7′ — 10,000
Not very rich, but possibly the nearest globular cluster to our solar system.

CENTAURUS

NGC 3766 — Open Cluster — 5.3 — 12′ — 100
A tightly packed, beautifully rich open cluster.

ω Centauri — Globular Cluster — 3.7 — 36.3′ — (See Map 5)

NGC 5460 — Open Cluster — 5.6 — 25′ — (See Map 5)

CARINA

NGC 2516 — Open Cluster — 3.8 — 30′ — 80
A rich open cluster with a bright red giant in the middle.

NGC 2808 — Globular Cluster — 6.3 — 14.8′
A very rich globular cluster.

NGC 3293 — Open Cluster — 4.7 — 6′
A rich, condensed cluster in very good company on the edge of the great Eta Carina Nebula. Excellent in a telescope or binoculars.

IC 2602 — Open Cluster — 1.9 — 50′ — 60

+Mel 101 — Open Cluster — 8.0 — 14′ — 50
IC 2602 is sometimes called the "Southern Pleiades." It is a large, cluster of bright stars with a smaller, fainter, but more densely packed neighbor, Mel 101.

NGC 3372 — Bright Nebula — — — 2°
The "Eta Carina" nebula or "Keyhole" nebula. The centerpiece of the entire southern Milky Way! This is the most luminous bright nebula in the sky. Binoculars will show the whole nebula in its gorgeous setting among dozens of open clusters and other wisps of nebulosity. With a small telescope you can wander across several fields of view without ever leaving the nebula!

NGC 3114 — Open Cluster — 4.2 — 35′
A bright, rich, and large open cluster, easy in binoculars or small telescope.

NGC 3532 — Open Cluster — 3.0 — 55′ — 150
A very large, very rich, and very bright resident of the Crux-Carina region.

Cr 240 — Open Cluster — 3.9 — 25′ — 30
A large cluster in an area full of clusters between Carina and Crux. Sweep the whole neighborhood for non-stop richness.

CRUX

NGC 4755 — Open Cluster — 4.2 — 10′
Called the "Jewel Box" with good reason. This impressive group is one of the most famous open clusters. It is notable for its high color contrast.

DORADO

LMC — Galaxy — 0.6 — 11°×9°
The Large Magellanic Cloud, our nearest galactic neighbor, possibly in the process of being cannibalized by our own much larger Milky Way galaxy. It is extremely active in star formation and consequently rich in nebulae and star clusters. A single telescope field of view will often show a half dozen or more nebulae! The galaxy as a whole can be appreciated with binoculars, but it will richly reward hours upon hours of exploration with telescopes of all sizes.

NGC 2070 — Cl w/Neb in LMC — 8.3 — 5′
The "Tarantula" nebula is the largest, brightest, and most beautiful nebula in the LMC, a region rich in bright nebulae! It is, in fact, one of the largest nebulae known anywhere in the universe! If it were as close as the Orion nebula it would occupy over 30° of the sky. It has a dense star cluster at its core surrounded by large symmetric wisps, looking more like a butterfly than a tarantula.

MUSCA

NGC 4372 — Globular Cluster — 7.8 — 18.6′

+NGC 4833 — Globular Cluster — 7.4 — 13.5′
Neither of these globulars is particularly rich, as globular clusters go, but they make a nice pair in this small constellation under the Southern Cross (Crux).

NORMA

NGC 6067 — Open Cluster — 5.6 — 13′ — 100
A bright, rich cluster that stands out even against the rich background of a Milky Way star cloud.

PAVO

NGC 6752 — Globular Cluster — 5.4 — 20.4′ — 100,000
This is one of the largest and brightest globular clusters in the sky.

TUCANA

SMC — Galaxy — 1.5 — 3.5°
The Small Magellanic Cloud is the Milky Way's second companion galaxy. It is classified as an irregular galaxy, appearing almost triangular. It is thought to be a flattened system partially tilted to our line of sight. It contains several nebulae and star clusters, but not nearly to the extent as in the LMC.

Name	Object Type	Mag	Size	# of Stars

TUCANA (Cont.)

47 Tucanae — Globular Cluster — 4.0 — 31.9′ — 270,000
47 Tuc has our vote for the most spectacular globular cluster in the entire sky. It is almost the same size and brightness as ω Centauri, but whereas ω Centauri is fairly uniform in brightness, 47 Tuc grows dramatically brighter toward the center. It appears as a bright, slightly fuzzy star to the naked eye, beautiful in binoculars or telescopes of any size, and increasingly beautiful with larger scopes.

NGC 362 — Globular Cluster — 6.6 — 13.9′
This rich globular cluster would get more attention elsewhere in the sky, but it is hard to take seriously when it is only a few fields of view away from 47 Tuc. After viewing 47 Tuc, look at NGC 362 to come back to reality.

VELA

NGC 2547 — Open Cluster — 4.7 — 20′ — (See Map 4)

IC 2391 — Open Cluster — 2.5 — 50′ — (See Map 4)

NGC 3201 — Globular Cluster — 6.8 — 18.2′ — (See Map 4)

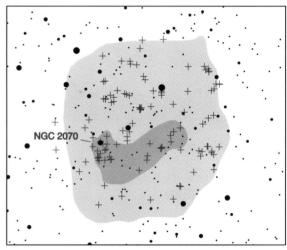

Large Magellanic Cloud (LMC). NGC 2070 and the other "+" marks indicate star clusters and nebulae within the LMC. 10° total field. Stars shown to Mag. 9.

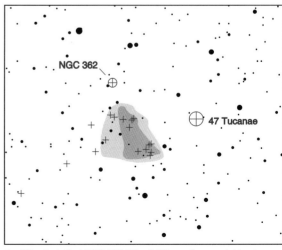

Small Magellanic Cloud (SMC). NGC 362 and 47 Tuc are foreground objects in our own galaxy. The "+" marks indicate star clusters and nebulae within the SMC. 10° total field. Stars shown to Mag. 9.

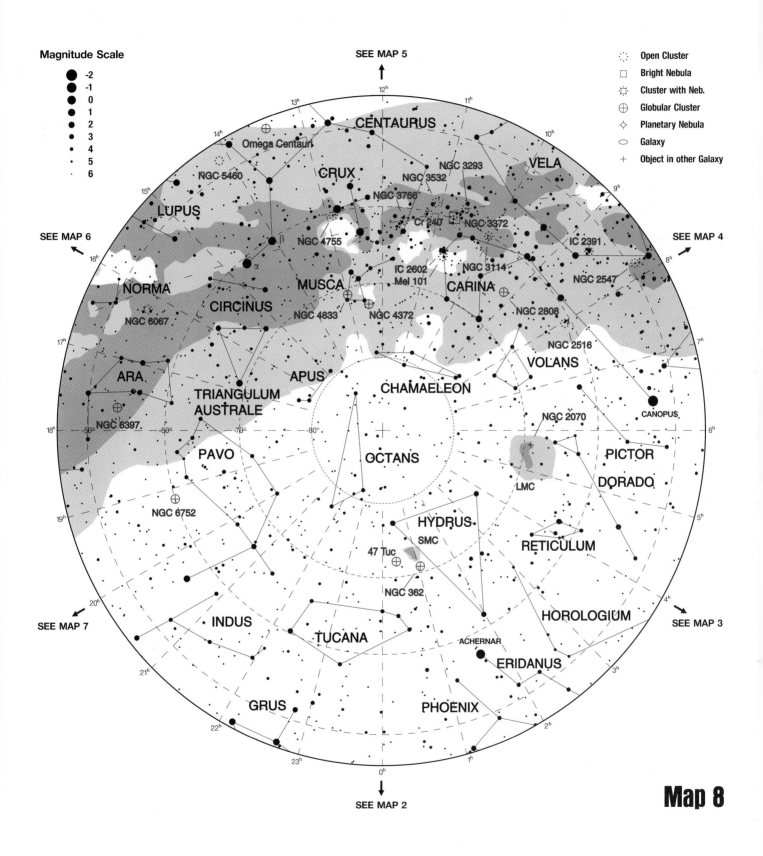

Magnitude Scale

- ● -2
- ● -1
- ● 0
- ● 1
- ● 2
- ● 3
- • 4
- • 5
- · 6

Open Cluster
Bright Nebula
Cluster with Neb.
Globular Cluster
Planetary Nebula
Galaxy
Object in other Galaxy

SEE MAP 5

SEE MAP 6

SEE MAP 4

SEE MAP 7

SEE MAP 3

SEE MAP 2

CENTAURUS
Omega Centauri
NGC 5460
CRUX
NGC 3532
NGC 3293
VELA
NGC 3766
LUPUS
NGC 4755
Cr 240
NGC 3372
IC 2391
β
IC 2602
NGC 3114
NGC 2547
α
Mel 101
MUSCA
NORMA
CARINA
NGC 4833
NGC 4372
CIRCINUS
NGC 2808
NGC 6067
NGC 2516
VOLANS
ARA
APUS
CHAMAELEON
NGC 2070
NGC 6397
TRIANGULUM
AUSTRALE
CANOPUS
PAVO
OCTANS
PICTOR
LMC
DORADO
NGC 6752
HYDRUS
SMC
RETICULUM
47 Tuc
HOROLOGIUM
NGC 362
INDUS
TUCANA
ACHERNAR
ERIDANUS
GRUS
PHOENIX

Map 8

Resource List

All of the references listed here are written for the layman and have been chosen for their excellent treatment of the subject: getting *you* acquainted with the sky.

BOOKS

Atlas of Deep Sky Splendors
by Hans Vehrenberg
Fourth Edition
Sky Publishing Corporation, Cambridge, Massachusetts
A beautiful photographic atlas with consistent size fields for each shot, making comparisons easy.

Observing Handbook And Catalogue Of Deep-Sky Objects
by Christian B. Luginbuhl and Brian A. Skiff
Cambridge University Press, Cambridge, Massachusetts
An excellent guide to observing skills. The sections preceding the catalogue are a wealth of useful concise information.
Each catalogued object is impeccably annotated.

Burnham's Celestial Handbook:
An Observer's Guide To The Universe Beyond The Solar System
by Robert Burnham, Jr.
Three Volumes
Dover Publications, Inc., New York
These three volumes have been a classic for many years. They are organized by constellation and contain a lifetime of accumulated information.

Sky Atlas 2000.0
by Wil Tirion
Sky Publishing Corporation, Cambridge, Massachusetts
Your next atlas! This has become the standard reference for serious amateurs.

Uranometria 2000.0
Two Volumes
by Wil Tirion, Barry Rappaport, George Lovi
Willmann-Bell, Inc., Richmond Virginia

Observing The Constellations
An A-Z Guide For The Amateur Astronomer
by John Sanford
Simon and Schuster, New York
Across from each constellation map is a facing page with a photo of the constellation in the same scale- a very useful device for recognizing the patterns.

The Sky: A User's Guide
by David H. Levy
Cambridge University Press, Cambridge, Massachusetts
We especially like Levy's introduction to variable star observing.

Star Names: Their Lore and Meaning
by Richard Hinckley Allen
Dover Publications, Inc., New York
Many's the time we sat in the car with Allen's Star Names, waiting for the clouds to pass.

The Star Atlas Companion Book
by Stephen Overholt
Owl Books
A very nice treatment of binary stars with sketches showing their position angles.

Galaxies
by Timothy Ferris
Stewart, Tabori & Chang, New York
Everything you ever wanted to know about galaxies- ours and others, beautifully illustrated. You'll want the paperback to pour over, and the hardbound to show off.

Exploring The Southern Sky
A Pictorial Atlas from the European Southern Observatory (ESO)
by Svend Laustsen, Claus Madsen, and Richard M. West
Springer-Verlag, New York
What Ferris does for galaxies, this does for the magnificent southern skies.

Exploring The Night Sky With Binoculars
by David Chandler
David Chandler Company, Springville, California
Illustrations by Don Davis show how objects appear visually, not photographically which can be quite different.

The Night Sky
by David Chandler Company
A specially designed low distortion planisphere for finding the constellations.

SOFTWARE

Deep Space
The Observer's Guide To The Night Sky
Produced by David Chandler Company
Software for IBM PCs

PERIODICALS

Astronomy Magazine
Kalmbach Publishing Co., Waukesha, Wisconsin
A monthly magazine for the astronomy hobbyist

Sky & Telescope Magazine
Sky Publishing Corp.
Cambridge, Massachusetts
Also monthly. Both magazines offer special rates if you are affiliated with a local astronomy club.

Astronomical Calendar (annual), *& Astronomical Companion*
by Guy Ottewell
Furman University, Greenville, South Carolina

The Observer's Handbook
Published annually by the Royal Astronomical Society of Canada
Standard equipment for your book bag.

...and for the southern hemisphere observers-
A Practical Guide To The Night Sky
by Ken Dawes, Peter Northfield, and Ken Wallace
Quasar Publishing, Strathfield NSW, Australia
Published annually, thoughtfully compiled for the folks down under!

And last but possibly the best resource of all, check your area for a local astronomy club. Other amateurs are a wealth of information and friendly help.